Ed Sheeran

WISE PUBLICATIONS
part of The Music Sales Group
London / New York / Paris / Sydney / Copenhagen / Berlin / Madrid / Hong Kong / Tokyo

Published by
Wise Publications
14-15 Berners Street, London W1T 3LJ, UK.

Exclusive Distributors:
Music Sales Limited
Distribution Centre, Newmarket Road,
Bury St Edmunds, Suffolk IP33 3YB, UK.

Music Sales Pty Limited
Units 3-4, 17 Willfox Street, Condell Park
NSW 2200, Australia.

Order No. AM1009338
ISBN: 978-1-78305-691-0
This book © Copyright 2014 Wise Publications,
a division of Music Sales Limited.

Edited by Jenni Norey.
Music arranged by Vasco Hexel.
Music processed by Paul Ewers Music Design.

Printed in the EU.

One

Words & Music by Ed Sheeran

'cause you are the on - ly one.

Stum-bl-ing half__ drunk,__

get - ting my - self__ lost,_____ I am so gone.

So tell me the way__ home.__ I lis-ten to sad__ songs,__ sing-ing a - bout__ love__

8

and where it goes wrong,_____

ooh._____

D.S. al Coda

Coda

you are the on - ly one._____

9

I'm A Mess

Words & Music by Ed Sheeran

11

Sing

Words & Music by Ed Sheeran & Pharrell Williams

need you darl - ing come on, set the tone.__ If you feel you're fall - ing, won't you let me know?__ Oh, oh,__

ooh.____   Oh, oh,____ ooh.____

If you love__ me come on, get in - volved__ feel it rush - ing through__ you from your head to toe.__ Oh, oh,__

ooh.____   Oh, oh,____ ooh.____   Sing!

then, we've got noth-ing to say __ and noth-ing to know but some-thing to drink __ and may-be some-thing to smoke. __

C#m

Let it go un - til our roads are changed, __ sing-ing "we found love in a lo - cal rave." __ No,

I don't real-ly know what I'm sup-posed to say. __ But I can just fi-gure it out and hope and pray. __ I

G#m

told her my name __ and said "it's nice to meet __ ya." Then she hand-ed me a bot-tle of wa-ter filled with te-qui-la.

20

I al-read-y know that she's a keep-er. Just from this one small act of kind-ness. I'm in

C#m

deep if an-y-bod-y finds out. I'm meant___ to drive home but I've drunk all of it now. Not

D.S. al Coda

so-ber-ing up, we just sit on the couch.___ One thing___ led to an-oth-er now she's kiss-ing my mouth.___ I

Coda   C#m   G#m

oh._____ Can you feel___ it? All the guys in here don't e-ven wan-na dance. Can you feel___

21

it? All that I can hear is mu-sic from the back. Can you feel___ it? Found you hid-ing here so

won't you take my hand,___ darl-ing, un-til the beat kicks in a-gain. Can you feel___

___ it? *Vocal ad lib.*

Sing! I

Don't

Words & Music by Ed Sheeran, Ali Jones-Muhammad, Raphael Saadiq,
Benjamin Levin, Conesha Owens & Dawn Robinson

Fm   Cm   Dᵇ   Eᵇ

I'm not real-ly look-ing for an-oth-er mis-take._ I called an old friend think-ing that the trou-ble would wait._ But then I
-sage_ was the on - ly way to reach her._Now she's stay-ing at my place and loves the way I treat_ her._ Sing-in' out A -

Fm   Cm   Dᵇ   Eᵇ

jump right in a week la-ter re-turned._ I reck-on she was on - ly look-ing for a lov-er to burn._ But I
-re - tha all o-ver the track like a fea - ture. And nev-er wants to sleep, I guess that I don't want to ei - ther.

Fm   Cm   Dᵇ   Eᵇ

gave her my time for two or three nights. Then I put it on pause un-til the mo-ment was right._ I went a -
But me and her we make mon-ey the same way. Four cit - ies, two planes the same_ day._

28

love.   I told her, she   knows.   Take   aim   and   re-

-load.____   I don't wan - na   know   that____   babe.   Ah,   la - ah - la -   la.

Verse 3:

[Knock, knock, knock] on my hotel door.
I don't even know if she knows what for.
She was crying on my shoulder.
I already told ya.
Trust and respect is what we do this for.
I never intended to be next.
But you didn't need to take him to bed, that's all.
And I never saw him as a threat.
Until you disappeared with him to have sex, of course.
It's not like we were both on tour.
We were staying on the same ****ing hotel floor.
And I wasn't looking for a promise to commitment.
But it was never just fun and I thought you were different.
This is not the way you realise what you wanted.
It's a bit too much too late if I'm honest.
All this time, god knows, I'm singin':

Nina

Words & Music by Ed Sheeran, Johnny McDaid, Jermaine Scott,
Jay Hippolyte & Isra Lohata

1. I met you when I
was a teen but then you were one as well.___ And I could
(2.) week-end in the win-ter, you'd be wear-ing my hood-ie with draw-
play a gui-tar___ just like ring-ing a bell. Some-times I
-strings pulled tight___ to keep your face from the cold. Tak-ing

32

home,_ no, no, oh,_ won't you leave me now. And I've been liv-ing on the

road,_ Ni - na. But then a-gain, you should know,_ Ni - na. 'Cause that's you and me,

both,_ no, no, oh,_ won't you leave me now, now._____

Photograph

Words & Music by Ed Sheeran & Johnny McDaid

1. Lov-ing can hurt.

Lov-ing can hurt_____ some-times.
(2.) Lov-ing can mend_____ your soul.

But it's the on -
And is the on -

L.H. 2° only

Bloodstream

Words & Music by Ed Sheeran, Gary Lightbody, Johnny McDaid,
Kesi Dryden, Piers Aggett & Amir Amor

1. I've been spin-ning now_ for time,   coup - le wom-en by_ my side.
2. I've been look - ing for a lov-er,   thought I'd find her in a bot-tle.

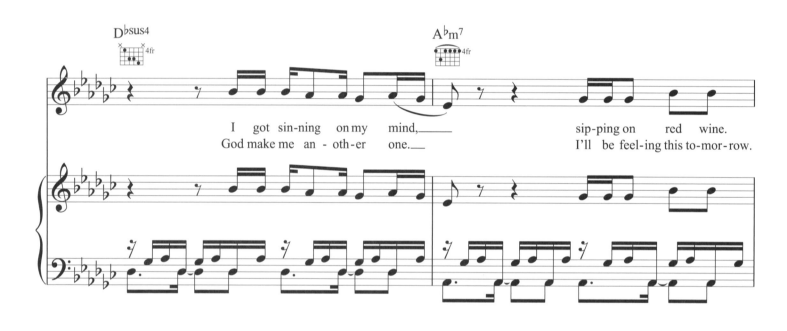

I got sin-ning on my mind,_____   sip-ping on red wine.
God make me an - oth-er one._   I'll be feel-ing this to-mor-row.

I've been sit-ting here_ for a - ges,_   rip-ping out_ the
Lord, for-give me for_ the things I've done._   I was nev-er meant

Mm, mm,____ mm, mm,____

____ mm, mm.____

Well, tell me when it kicks in. All the voi - ces in my

mind call - ing out a - cross the line. All the voi - ces in my

51

Tenerife Sea

Words & Music by Ed Sheeran, Johnny McDaid & Foy Vance

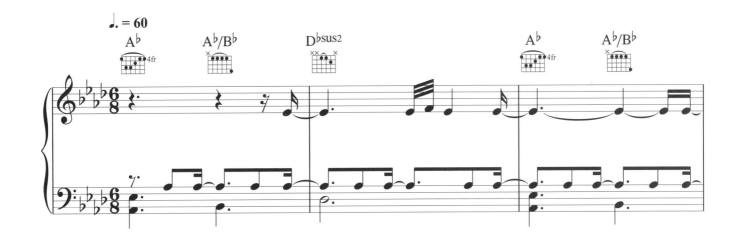

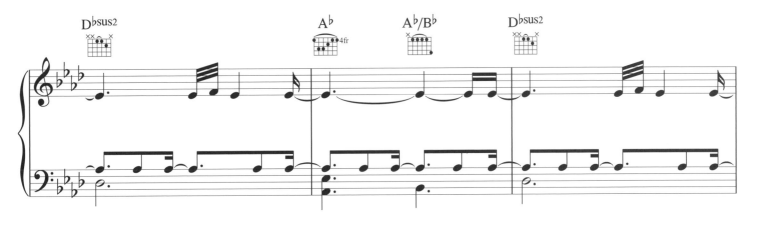

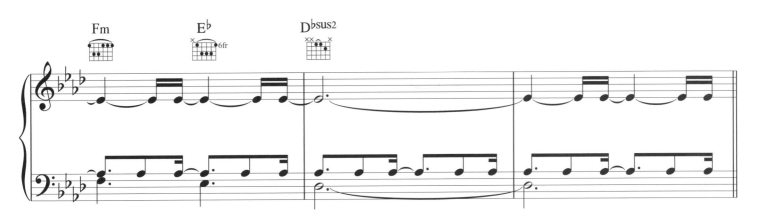

1. You look so won-der-ful in your dress.
2. You look so beau-ti-ful in this light,

I love you hair like that.
your sil-hou-ette o-ver me.

The way it falls on the side
The way it brings out the blue

of your neck,
in your eyes is the Te-ner-ife

down your shoul-ders and back.
Sea. And

54

Runaway

Words & Music by Ed Sheeran & Pharrell Williams

The Man

Words & Music by Ed Sheeran

1. *Now, I don't wanna hate you,*

just wish you'd never gone for the man and waited two weeks at least before you let him take you, I stayed true
(2.) *tend to zone out up in my headphone to "Holocene". You promised your body but I'm away so much, I stay more celibate than in a*
(Verse 3 see block lyrics)

I kinda knew you liked the dude from private school, he's waiting for the time to move I knew he had his eyes on you.
monastery. I'm not cut out for life on the road, 'cause I didn't know I'd miss you this much and at the time we'd just go,

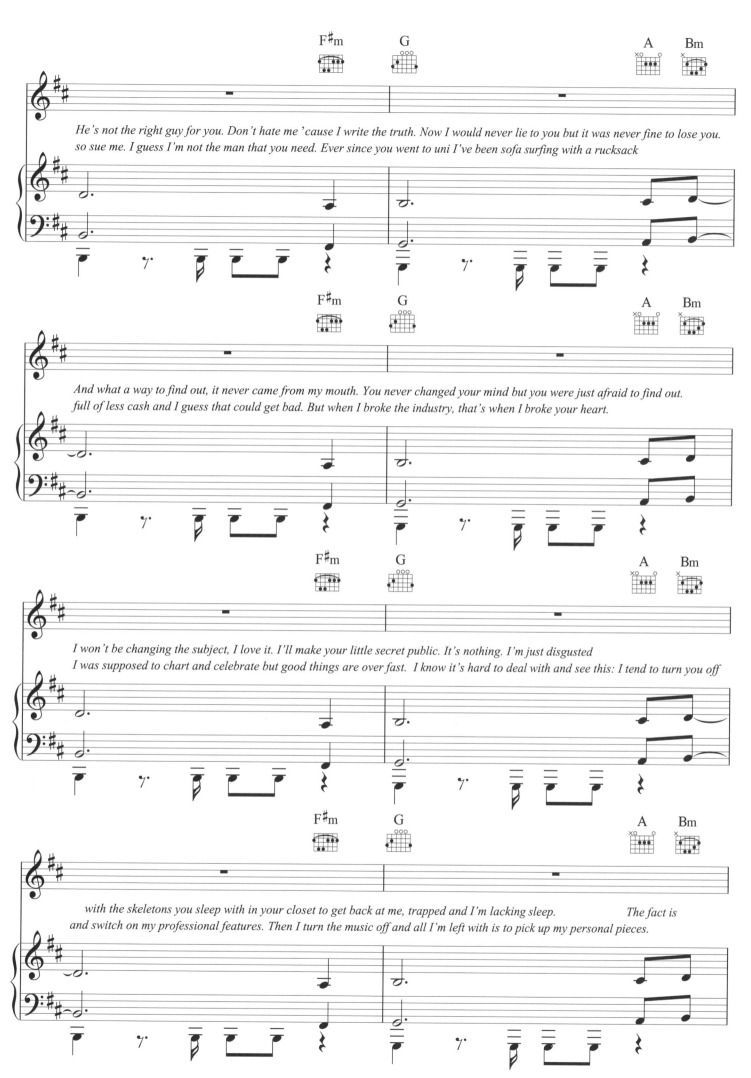

He's not the right guy for you. Don't hate me 'cause I write the truth. Now I would never lie to you but it was never fine to lose you.
so sue me. I guess I'm not the man that you need. Ever since you went to uni I've been sofa surfing with a rucksack

And what a way to find out, it never came from my mouth. You never changed your mind but you were just afraid to find out.
full of less cash and I guess that could get bad. But when I broke the industry, that's when I broke your heart.

I won't be changing the subject, I love it. I'll make your little secret public. It's nothing. I'm just disgusted
I was supposed to chart and celebrate but good things are over fast. I know it's hard to deal with and see this: I tend to turn you off

with the skeletons you sleep with in your closet to get back at me, trapped and I'm lacking sleep.   The fact is
and switch on my professional features. Then I turn the music off and all I'm left with is to pick up my personal pieces.

Verse 3:

Since you left I've given up my days off.
It's what I need to stay strong.
I know you have a day job but mine is 24/7.
I feel like writing a book, I guess I lied in the hook.
'Cause I still love you and I need you by my side if I could.
The irony is if my career and music didn't exist,
In six years, yeah, you'd probably be my wife with a kid.
I'm frightened to think if I depend on cider and drink
And lighting a spliff, I fall into a spiral and it's just hiding my
Misguiding thoughts that I'm trying to kill.
And I'd be writing my will before I'm 27.
I'll die from a thrill, go down in history as just a wasted talent.
Can I face the challenge or did I make a mistake erasing?
It's only therapy, my thoughts just get ahead of me.
Eventually I'll be fine, I know that it was never meant to be.
Either way I guess, I'm not prepared. But I'll say this:
These things happen for a reason and you can't change.
Take my apology. I'm sorry for the honesty, but I had to get this off my chest.

Thinking Out Loud

Words & Music by Ed Sheeran & Amy Wadge

72

Afire Love

Words & Music by Ed Sheeran, Johnny McDaid,
Foy Vance & Christophe Beck

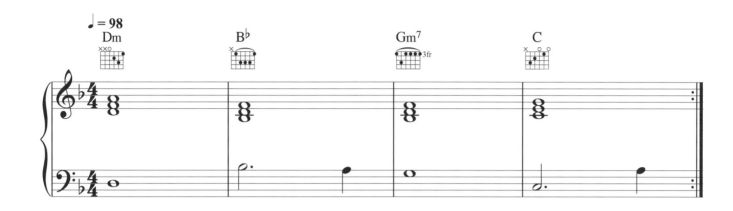

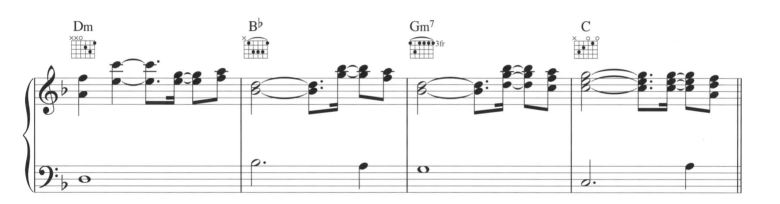

1. Things were all good yes-ter-day____ and then the dev-il took your mem-o-ry.

2. Things were all good yes-ter-day____ and then the dev-il took your breath a-way.

Take It Back

Words & Music by Ed Sheeran & Johnny McDaid

1. *I'm not a rapper, I'm a singer with a flow. I've got a habit for spitting quicker lyrics, you know.*
(2.) *with the rhythm and blues, with my rap pack I'll be singing the news, tryin' to act like Jack Black when*
(Verse 3 see block lyrics)

You find me ripping the written out of the pages they sit in. I never want to get bitten 'cause plagiarism is hidden.
I bring it to school. I make a beat with my feet by just hittin' the loop, bringing the lyrics to prove that I can fit in these shoes.

Watch how I sit on the rhythm, prisoner with a vision. Signed to a label, but didn't listen to any criticism.
I give you the truth through the vocal booth. And stars burst out on the scene like an opal fruit. They try to

Thought you knew but you didn't. So perk your ears up and listen. Studio is a system and you could say that I'm driven.
take aim like Beckham when he goes to shoot. But then again that's what they're supposed to do. And I'm supposed to be calm.

And now it's on to the next saga. We drink the best lager. I'll never try to win you over like your stepfather.
I tattooed the lyrics onto my arm. Whispering everything that happens is from now on. I'll be ready to start again

I do my own thing now and get respect after. And I'm avoiding the 'caine like it was Get Carter.
by the end of the song. Still they're claiming that I handled it wrong. But then I've never had an enemy, except the NME.

For four years I never had a place to stay. But it's safe to say that it kept me grounded like a paperweight.
But I'll be selling twice as many copies as the magazines will ever be

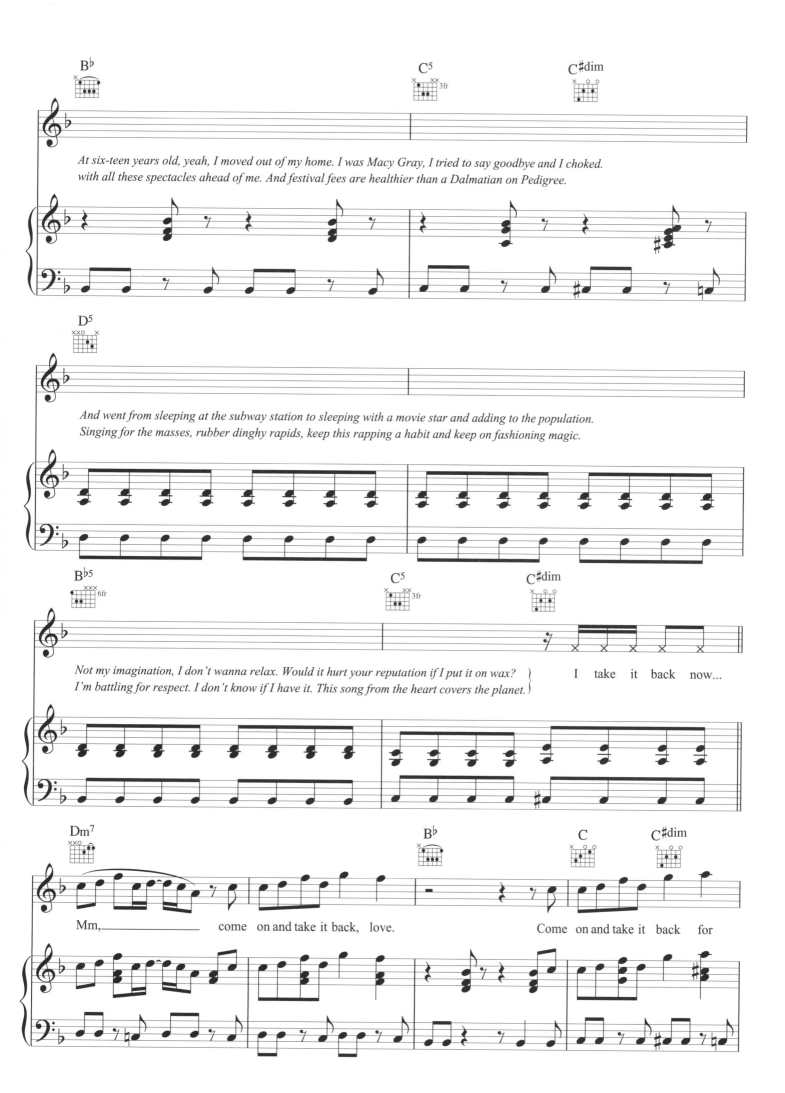

At six-teen years old, yeah, I moved out of my home. I was Macy Gray, I tried to say goodbye and I choked.
with all these spectacles ahead of me. And festival fees are healthier than a Dalmatian on Pedigree.

And went from sleeping at the subway station to sleeping with a movie star and adding to the population.
Singing for the masses, rubber dinghy rapids, keep this rapping a habit and keep on fashioning magic.

Not my imagination, I don't wanna relax. Would it hurt your reputation if I put it on wax?
I'm battling for respect. I don't know if I have it. This song from the heart covers the planet.

I take it back now...

Mm,_____ come on and take it back, love.

Come on and take it back for

on and take it back for us.____ Don't you fade in-to the back, love.

No._____ Mhm..._____

Verse 3:

And take it back now.
Now, I don't ever wanna be perfect.
'Cause I'm a singer that you never wanna see shirtless.
And I accept the fact that someone's got to win worst-dressed.
Taken my first steps into the scene, giving me focus.
Putting on a brave face, like Timothy Dalton.
Considering a name change, thinking it was hopeless.
Rhyming over recordings, avoiding tradition.
'Cause every day's a lyric and the melody can be written.
Now absence can make your heart ache,
But drinking absinthe can change your mind-state, vividly.
Need to let my liver be. And I'll say it again:
Living life on the edge with a close handful of friends
It's good advice from the man that took his life on the road with me.
And I hope to see him blowing up globally
'Cause that's how it's supposed to be. I'm screaming out vocally.
It might seem totally impossible, achieving life's dreams.
But I just write schemes.
I'm never having a stylist, giving me tight jeans.
Madison Square Garden is where I might be.
But more likely you find me in the back room of a dive bar with my mates.
Having a pint of McDaid discussing records we made.
And every single second knowing that we'll never betray the way we were raised,
Remembering our background, sat down.
That's how we plan it out. It's time to take it back now.

Shirtsleeves

Words & Music by Ed Sheeran

your eyes,___ your eyes, your eyes,___ your eyes, your___

eyes.___

Even My Dad Does Sometimes

Words & Music by Ed Sheeran & Amy Wadge

90

93

I See Fire

Words & Music by Ed Sheeran

Freely, rubato

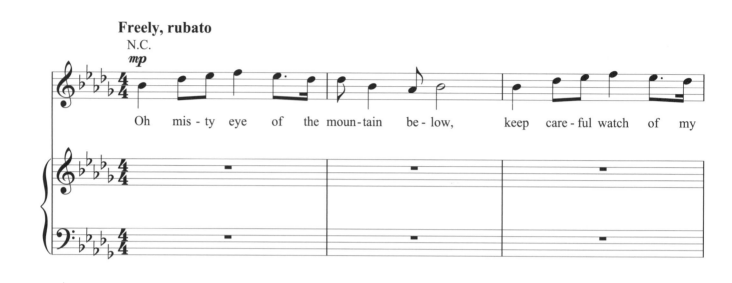

Oh mis-ty eye of the moun-tain be-low, keep care-ful watch of my

broth-er's souls. And should the sky___ be filled with fire___ and smoke,

___ keep watch-ing o-ver Dur - in's Sons.

Moderately slow ♩ = 76

Guitar chords with capo, 6th fret

1. If this is to end in fire, then we should all burn to-geth-er, watch the

flames climb high into the night. Call-ing out fath-er, oh,

stand by and we will watch the flames burn au - burn on the

* Melody sung in octaves throughout. †Symbols in parentheses represent chord names with respect to capoed guitar.
Symbols above represent actual sounding chords.

95

456789